Copyright © 1988 Alan Marks
First published 1988 by
Blackie and Son Ltd

British Library Cataloguing in Publication Data

Marks, Alan
    Childe Roland
    I. Title II. Series
    823'.914[J]

    ISBN: 0-216-92356-5

Blackie and Son Ltd
7 Leicester Place
London WC2H 7BP

First American edition published in 1988 by
Peter Bedrick Books
2112 BROADWAY
New York NY 10023

Library of Congress Cataloging-in-Publication Data
Marks, Alan. 1957
    Childe Roland: an English folk tale/retold and
illustrated by Alan Marks.
    p. cm. — (Folk tales of the world)
    Summary: Childe Roland makes a dangerous journey
into Elfland to rescue his sister and brothers from
enchantment.
    ISBN: 0-87226-400-9
    [1. Fairy tales. 2. Folklore-England.] I. Title. II Series.
PZ7.M343CH 1988.
398.2'1'0942-dc 19
[E]

**Printed in Spain by
Salingraf, S.A.L.**

An English Folk Tale

Childe Roland

Folk Tales of the World

Retold and illustrated by
ALAN MARKS

Blackie
London

Bedrick/Blackie
New York

One bright morning in May the young prince, Childe Roland, and his sister, Burd Ellen, went out to the churchyard to play with their golden ball. Laughing and shouting they ran round the trees and gravestones until Childe Roland threw the ball so high into the air that it flew over the roof of the church. Burd Ellen ran round the church after it, but although Childe Roland waited and waited she never came back. He searched every corner of the church and every inch of the churchyard but she had vanished without a trace.

Childe Roland went back home and told his father, the king, and his mother, the queen, and his two brothers what had happened. The eldest brother decided that he would go to the wizard Merlin and ask him how he could find his sister.

'Burd Ellen ran widdershins around the church,' said Merlin, 'that is, she ran contrary to the course of the sun. And now the King of Elfland has taken her away to his kingdom. To find her you must go to the Dark Tower and only the bravest of knights should dare go there.'

'Tell me how I can win her back and I will try,' said the eldest brother. So Merlin taught him everything he needed to know and off went the eldest brother in search of Burd Ellen. But he was never seen again.

Then the second brother went to Merlin. And he too set off in search of Burd Ellen and was never seen again.

Now Childe Roland was the only brother left. It was his turn to go to the wizard.

'How can I win my sister back?' he said.

'There are two things you must do,' said Merlin, 'and both are more difficult than they seem. Firstly, if anyone speaks to you in Elfland before you meet Burd Ellen you must cut off their head. Secondly, you must not eat a single crumb or drink a single drop while you are in Elfland — or you will never see this earth again.'

Childe Roland thanked the wizard for his help and, taking
up his father's sword, he set off in search of his sister.

He went along, and along, and along and still further
along until he met a horse-herd feeding some horses.
When Childe Roland saw their flaming eyes he knew
that these were the horses of the King of Elfland and
that he was now in the Elfin kingdom.

'Can you tell me the way to the Dark Tower?' Childe
Roland asked.

'I cannot,' said the horse-herd, 'but if you go a little
further you'll meet a cow-herd who may help you.'

Without another word Childe Roland struck off the
horse-herd's head, for this is what Merlin had told him
to do.

He went along, and along, and along and still further along until he met a cow-herd.

'Can you tell me the way to the Dark Tower?' Childe Roland asked.

'I cannot,' said the cow-herd, 'but if you go a little further you'll meet a hen-wife who may help you.'

Without another word Childe Roland struck off the cow-herd's head and rode on.

He went along, and along, and along and still further along until he met a hen-wife.

'Can you tell me the way to the Dark Tower?' Childe Roland asked.

'If you go a little further you will come to a high round hill with terraces on every side. Go round the hill three times widdershins, each time saying:

Open door! Open door!

And let me come in.

Then you will find the Dark Tower.'

And Childe Roland struck off the hen-wife's head as Merlin had told him to do and rode on.

He went along, and along, and along and still further along until he saw a steep terraced hill rising up before him, just as the hen-wife had said. In its side was a small wooden door, tightly shut.

Childe Roland ran round the hill widdershins three times, each time saying:

> Open door! Open door!
> And let me come in.

And the third time the door opened and Childe Roland entered the Dark Tower.

The door clicked shut behind him. He expected to find himself in darkness but instead there was a dim glow as there is at twilight. Around him arched high walls of rough transparent rock encrusted with sheepsilver, rock spar and other bright stones. And ahead of him stood two great doors of solid oak.

Through the doors Childe Roland went, and suddenly
he found himself in a great hall as high and broad as the
hill itself. Pillars of gold and silver stretched up to the
roof, wreathed and fretted with garlands of diamonds,
emeralds, sapphires and rubies. From a gold chain in the
centre of the room hung a huge hollow pearl with a
garnet in the middle, which cast rays of light like the
setting sun through the room.

And there, at the end of the hall, on a beautiful couch
of silk and velvet, sat Burd Ellen combing her golden
hair with a silver comb.

When she saw Childe Roland she stood up and cried out, 'You should never have come here! Even if you had a hundred lives you should not have come!'

They sat down together and she told him how their two brothers had been enchanted and how they lay as if dead in tombs of stone.

After a while Childe Roland felt hungry and, forgetting what Merlin had said, asked his sister if there was something he could eat. Burd Ellen looked at him sadly, but she was under a spell and could give him no warning, so she fetched him a gold basin of bread and milk.

Childe Roland raised the bowl to his lips but then he looked at his sister and remembered everything Merlin had said. He smashed the bowl to the ground. 'Not a crumb will I eat and not a drop will I drink until you are free!' he cried.

Then suddenly in the passageway they heard the sound of approaching footsteps and with a roar the King of Elfland burst into the hall. Childe Roland drew his sword and they fought and fought, until finally Childe Roland forced the king to his knees.

'Mercy!' cried the king.

'Then free my sister and my brothers,' said Childe Roland.

The king opened a chest and took from it a small bottle of blood-red liquid. He put a little on the eyes, ears, lips, nose and fingertips of the two brothers and they sprang to life. Then he spoke a few words to Burd Ellen and the spell over her was lifted.

Childe Roland led his sister and two brothers from the Dark Tower. And they left Elfland and returned joyfully together to their own kingdom.

7/96 — 6/95 -12